8 Weeks Towards
Maximum
Health

A guided journal to help you focus, feel and perform better

KATY SHERIDAN

ISBN: 978-1-9163500-0-7

Further resources, information, podcasts and training are
available from Maximum Edge CIC – a community interest
company based in the UK, specialising in the development
of people, with the aim of strengthening communities.

Website: www.maximumedge.org.uk
Twitter: @MaxEdgeCIC
Facebook: @MaxEdgeCIC
YouTube: Maximum Edge

For audio content, ask your smart-speaker to
"play Maximum Edge CIC Podcast Channel" or find our
channel on Podbean, Spotify and Apple Podcasts

10 9 8 7 6 5 4 3 2 1

To all our loved ones, here and elsewhere.
Bet you weren't expecting this!

This guided journal can be used as a standalone item or
alongside our podcasts, resources, handouts and videos,
as part of our wider work.

www.maximumedge.org.uk

CONTENTS

You are never too old to set another goal
or to dream a new dream

C.S. LEWIS

INTRODUCTION

We all have a tendency to forget about the little things and focus on the big things in life. Big changes, big worries (or lots of little worries), big goals. It can be great to 'think big' but forgetting about the little things in life doesn't allow us to appreciate all the achievements we make every day - or to be grateful for the things and people we have around us.

This 8-week motivational life journal gives you a place to record your goals and achievements, improve habits, and ultimately feel better by being consciously self-aware more often.

Writing things down helps us to de-clutter our minds and gain some clarity from the day to day 'mind-chat' which can sometimes take over. Seeing our thoughts on paper can give us clarity and help us identify what it is that we really want. The next step would be to share these goals and dreams with people we trust. But for now, this journal is your stepping stone to a happier, healthier, more focused you.

Things to remember:

1. This is *your* book.

2. Nobody needs to see it.

3. Your writing doesn't need to be perfect.

4. You can make mistakes.

5. You might miss the odd day.

Take pressure off yourself and use this journal as your kick-start towards a *Better You*.

WHEEL OF LIFE

Now is a good time to review where you are in your life **now**. Not where you have been, or where you want to be, but be truthful with yourself about how you are living life today, this week.

A tool we can use to do this is the Wheel of Life. You will find a blank wheel on the following page which, once completed, will give you an indication of areas of your life which you may choose to work on over the next 8 weeks.

The 8 sections of the Wheel represent your life.

- 4 categories are completed for you. Complete the other 4 categories to make the wheel meaningful to you.
- Next, rank your level of satisfaction with each category out of 10 by drawing a line to create a new outer edge (see example). Use the centre of the wheel as 0 (totally unsatisfied) and the outer edge as 10 (completely satisfied)
- Note that very few people will mark 10 on all - or any - of their categories!
- When you have completed the wheel, the new shape represents your Wheel of Life and is your starting point from today.

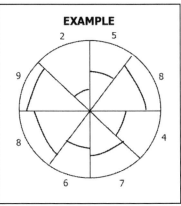

3

MY WHEEL OF LIFE

COMPLETED ON:_____

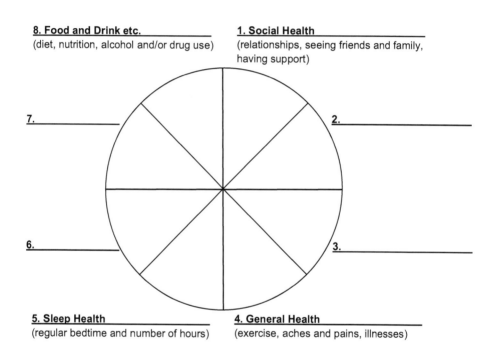

8. Food and Drink etc._____
(diet, nutrition, alcohol and/or drug use)

1. Social Health_____
(relationships, seeing friends and family, having support)

7._____

2._____

6._____

3._____

5. Sleep Health_____
(regular bedtime and number of hours)

4. General Health_____
(exercise, aches and pains, illnesses)

*You can use any categories you want for your wheel. Some examples which have been used in the past include motivation, work-life balance, relaxing, being professional in work, patience, confidence, practicing hobbies, and positive thinking.

REVERSE BUCKET LIST

To continue on this journey, we now need to look back. Set some time aside to stop and really think about all the positive things you have achieved in your life so far. Forget about the things you haven't done yet and the things you feel that you have missed out on. Focus purely on the things you have achieved. Write them all down. Every single thing. It could be anything: learning to swim, caring for a relative, travelling the world, getting promoted, finishing that boxset, trying a new food, ringing a friend, joining a club. Once you start, you might find it hard to stop.

Come back to it at any time to read through your achievements and add more to your "Reverse Bucket List".

My reverse bucket list (everything I have achieved in my life):

_____

_____

_____

_____

_____

Keep Going!

GOAL SETTING

Having completed your Wheel of Life and started your Reverse Bucket list, you now have a starting point from where you can go forward. You will have done some of the things on your list alone, and others with help from family, friends, colleagues and professionals. You may be able to identify people who support you, whatever you do in life. And you may also see just how much you have achieved and do achieve by being determined and self-motivated.

Goal setting can be obvious to some, while it takes a bit more work for others. What is it you want to achieve in 8 weeks? Do you want to see friends more, join a club, lose weight, worry less, drink less alcohol? Whatever it is, now is the time to think about setting some goals which are realistic but will still challenge you so that you feel a sense of achievement when you meet those goals. At the end of the 8 weeks, you may even add some of your achievements to your Reverse Bucket List!

Goals are personal to each individual. They can be anything. They are *your* goals, but the best, most achievable goals are SMART goals.

SMART goals are:

- **S**pecific
- **M**easurable
- **A**chievable
- **R**ealistic
- **T**ime-based

If your goal(s) meet all or most of these criteria, there is a higher likelihood that you are going to achieve them.

Over to you.

My Ultimate Goals to achieve in the next 8 weeks are:
(set as many as you want)

HOW TO USE THIS JOURNAL

Choose a time in your day when you are going to use your journal. You might want to try different times to find out when suits you best. First thing in the morning or last thing at night often work well. As long as you are not too tired and won't be distracted, you can use your journal whenever you want.

You will find a new section for each week, plus a 4 weekly review and an 8-week reflection. If you miss a couple of days don't worry about it! Just get back on track as soon as you can.

At the start of each week set your goals. This is where you can set smaller tasks towards the bigger goals which you set on page 8. Breaking large goals down into manageable tasks makes them more achievable. For example, on week one, your health goal might be to exercise for 30 mins on one day. You will probably want to alter this slightly each week, as you feel your motivation and energy levels increasing, so that by week 8 your health goal might be to exercise for 30 minutes on *three* days.

It's entirely up to you. As long as you keep your goals (and your smaller tasks) 'SMART', you should start to see yourself progressing towards them.

When you have set your goals for the week, you then have space each day to plan and reflect on what that day has given you, and what you have achieved. If you choose to complete the journal in the morning, you can reflect on the day before whilst focusing on your tasks ahead.

If you can't think of something to write sometimes, there is no pressure to complete every section every day, but once you get in to the habit of stopping and thinking, you will probably surprise yourself with how much of it you *can* complete.

There is space every day for you to add your own notes to make this journal entirely your own, and there is also a To Do list area. However, use this with caution! Don't let it become your day to day list of jobs that need doing, people you need to email etc. Keep it brief and specifically focused on that week's goals.

Once you are ready…

BEGIN

My social goal this week is:

My health goal this week is:

My food and drink goal this week is:

My sleep goal this week is:

My tasks towards my main goals are:

To Do List

Monday

I am grateful for: _____

I smiled when: _____

A challenge I overcame today: _____

_____

Something I achieved today: _____

_____

Tuesday

I am grateful for: _____

I smiled when: _____

A challenge I overcame today: _____

_____

Something I achieved today: _____

_____

Wednesday

I am grateful for: _____

I smiled when: _____

A challenge I overcame today: _____

_____

Something I achieved today: _____

_____

Thursday

I am grateful for: _____

I smiled when: _____

A challenge I overcame today: _____

_____

Something I achieved today: _____

_____

Friday

I am grateful for: _____

I smiled when: _____

A challenge I overcame today: _____

_____

Something I achieved today: _____

_____

Saturday

I am grateful for: _____

I smiled when: _____

A challenge I overcame today: _____

_____

Something I achieved today: _____

_____

Sunday

I am grateful for:

I smiled when:

A challenge I overcame today:

Something I achieved today:

My notes:

Each journey starts with the first step.

CHINESE PROVERB

My social goal this week is:

My health goal this week is:

My food and drink goal this week is:

My sleep goal this week is:

My tasks towards my main goals are:

To Do List

Monday

I am grateful for: _____

I smiled when: _____

A challenge I overcame today: _____

_____

Something I achieved today: _____

_____

Tuesday

I am grateful for: _____

I smiled when: _____

A challenge I overcame today: _____

_____

Something I achieved today: _____

_____

Wednesday

I am grateful for: _____

I smiled when: _____

A challenge I overcame today: _____

_____

Something I achieved today: _____

_____

Thursday

I am grateful for: _____

I smiled when: _____

A challenge I overcame today: _____

_____

Something I achieved today: _____

_____

Friday

I am grateful for: _____

I smiled when: _____

A challenge I overcame today: _____

_____

Something I achieved today: _____

_____

Saturday

I am grateful for: _____

I smiled when: _____

A challenge I overcame today: _____

_____

Something I achieved today: _____

_____

Sunday

I am grateful for:

I smiled when:

A challenge I overcame today:

Something I achieved today:

My notes:

You must do the things you think you cannot do.

ELEANOR ROOSEVELT (1884-1962)

My social goal this week is:

My health goal this week is:

My food and drink goal this week is:

My sleep goal this week is:

My tasks towards my main goals are:

To Do List

Monday

I am grateful for: _____

I smiled when: _____

A challenge I overcame today: _____

_____

Something I achieved today: _____

_____

Tuesday

I am grateful for: _____

I smiled when: _____

A challenge I overcame today: _____

_____

Something I achieved today: _____

_____

Wednesday

I am grateful for: _____

I smiled when: _____

A challenge I overcame today: _____

_____

Something I achieved today: _____

_____

Thursday

I am grateful for: _____

I smiled when: _____

A challenge I overcame today: _____

_____

Something I achieved today: _____

_____

Friday

I am grateful for: _____

I smiled when: _____

A challenge I overcame today: _____

_____

Something I achieved today: _____

_____

Saturday

I am grateful for: _____

I smiled when: _____

A challenge I overcame today: _____

_____

Something I achieved today: _____

_____

Sunday

I am grateful for: _____

I smiled when: _____

A challenge I overcame today: _____

_____

Something I achieved today: _____

_____

_____

My notes: _____

_____

_____

_____

_____

_____

_____

_____

_____

_____

_____

The future depends on what you do today.

MAHATMA GANDHI (1869-1948)

My social goal this week is:

My health goal this week is:

My food and drink goal this week is:

My sleep goal this week is:

My tasks towards my main goals are:

To Do List

Monday

I am grateful for: _____

I smiled when: _____

A challenge I overcame today: _____

_____

Something I achieved today: _____

_____

Tuesday

I am grateful for: _____

I smiled when: _____

A challenge I overcame today: _____

_____

Something I achieved today: _____

_____

Wednesday

I am grateful for: _____

I smiled when: _____

A challenge I overcame today: _____

_____

Something I achieved today: _____

_____

Thursday

I am grateful for:

I smiled when:

A challenge I overcame today:

Something I achieved today:

Friday

I am grateful for:

I smiled when:

A challenge I overcame today:

Something I achieved today:

Saturday

I am grateful for:

I smiled when:

A challenge I overcame today:

Something I achieved today:

Sunday

I am grateful for:

I smiled when:

A challenge I overcame today:

Something I achieved today:

My notes:

HALFWAY THERE

You are halfway there! How do you feel?

Make a point now of looking back to the start of this process and remembering how you felt *then*. Were you excited? Motivated? Daunted?

Have you already achieved things which you can add to your Reverse Bucket List? If you haven't, there are still 4 weeks left, so no need to panic or feel under pressure. You are in control of the goals you have set for yourself.

By now you might have started to notice patterns and triggers in your life which cause you to feel and behave more (and less) positively than at other times. Be aware of the things which cause you to react less positively and instead focus on those things which cause you to feel positive, motivated, and to treat others and yourself well. Use this as your encouragement to continue.

If you have started to or increased exercise, how does your body feel? Are you less stressed? Do you sleep better? Can you concentrate for longer? If you are having any issues, remember there is lots of information out there which can help you to find the right routine for you.

All these subtle changes that you are noticing are adding up to a better you.

Stay focused on the goals which you set. Go back and review them.

Are they still relevant and achievable? If you have already achieved one or more of them, think about setting some new ones to work towards.

Use this half-way point to look backwards and then to look forwards to the next 4 weeks.

My notes:

_____

_____

_____

_____

_____

_____

_____

_____

_____

_____

_____

_____

_____

_____

CONTINUE

My social goal this week is:

My health goal this week is:

My food and drink goal this week is:

My sleep goal this week is:

My tasks towards my main goals are:

To Do List

Monday

I am grateful for: _____

I smiled when: _____

A challenge I overcame today: _____

_____

Something I achieved today: _____

_____

Tuesday

I am grateful for: _____

I smiled when: _____

A challenge I overcame today: _____

_____

Something I achieved today: _____

_____

Wednesday

I am grateful for: _____

I smiled when: _____

A challenge I overcame today: _____

_____

Something I achieved today: _____

_____

Thursday

I am grateful for: _____

I smiled when: _____

A challenge I overcame today: _____

_____

Something I achieved today: _____

_____

Friday

I am grateful for: _____

I smiled when: _____

A challenge I overcame today: _____

_____

Something I achieved today: _____

_____

Saturday

I am grateful for: _____

I smiled when: _____

A challenge I overcame today: _____

_____

Something I achieved today: _____

_____

Sunday

I am grateful for: _____

I smiled when: _____

A challenge I overcame today: _____

_____

Something I achieved today: _____

_____

_____

My notes: _____

_____

_____

_____

_____

_____

_____

_____

_____

_____

_____

If you're walking down the right path and you're willing to keep walking, eventually you'll make progress.

BARACK OBAMA

My social goal this week is:

My health goal this week is:

My food and drink goal this week is:

My sleep goal this week is:

My tasks towards my main goals are:

To Do List

Monday

I am grateful for:

I smiled when:

A challenge I overcame today:

Something I achieved today:

Tuesday

I am grateful for:

I smiled when:

A challenge I overcame today:

Something I achieved today:

Wednesday

I am grateful for:

I smiled when:

A challenge I overcame today:

Something I achieved today:

Thursday

I am grateful for: _____

I smiled when: _____

A challenge I overcame today: _____

_____

Something I achieved today: _____

_____

Friday

I am grateful for: _____

I smiled when: _____

A challenge I overcame today: _____

_____

Something I achieved today: _____

_____

Saturday

I am grateful for: _____

I smiled when: _____

A challenge I overcame today: _____

_____

Something I achieved today: _____

_____

Sunday

I am grateful for: _____

I smiled when: _____

A challenge I overcame today: _____

_____

Something I achieved today: _____

_____

_____

My notes: _____

_____

_____

_____

_____

_____

_____

_____

_____

_____

_____

Nothing can dim the light that shines within you.

MAYA ANGELOU (1928-2014)

My social goal this week is:

_____

My health goal this week is:

_____

My food and drink goal this week is:

_____

My sleep goal this week is:

_____

My tasks towards my main goals are:

To Do List

Monday

I am grateful for: _____

I smiled when: _____

A challenge I overcame today: _____

_____

Something I achieved today: _____

_____

Tuesday

I am grateful for: _____

I smiled when: _____

A challenge I overcame today: _____

_____

Something I achieved today: _____

_____

Wednesday

I am grateful for: _____

I smiled when: _____

A challenge I overcame today: _____

_____

Something I achieved today: _____

_____

Thursday

I am grateful for: _____

I smiled when: _____

A challenge I overcame today: _____

_____

Something I achieved today: _____

_____

Friday

I am grateful for: _____

I smiled when: _____

A challenge I overcame today: _____

_____

Something I achieved today: _____

_____

Saturday

I am grateful for: _____

I smiled when: _____

A challenge I overcame today: _____

_____

Something I achieved today: _____

_____

Sunday

I am grateful for:

I smiled when:

A challenge I overcame today:

Something I achieved today:

My notes:

Success is not final. Failure is not fatal.

*It is the **courage to continue** that counts.*

WINSTON CHURCHILL (1874-1965)

My social goal this week is:

My health goal this week is:

My food and drink goal this week is:

My sleep goal this week is:

My tasks towards my main goals are:

To Do List

Monday

I am grateful for:

I smiled when:

A challenge I overcame today:

Something I achieved today:

Tuesday

I am grateful for:

I smiled when:

A challenge I overcame today:

Something I achieved today:

Wednesday

I am grateful for:

I smiled when:

A challenge I overcame today:

Something I achieved today:

Thursday

I am grateful for: _____

I smiled when: _____

A challenge I overcame today: _____

_____

Something I achieved today: _____

_____

_____

Friday

I am grateful for: _____

I smiled when: _____

A challenge I overcame today: _____

_____

Something I achieved today: _____

_____

_____

Saturday

I am grateful for: _____

I smiled when: _____

A challenge I overcame today: _____

_____

Something I achieved today: _____

_____

Sunday

I am grateful for:

I smiled when:

A challenge I overcame today:

Something I achieved today:

My notes:

8 WEEKS - YOU'VE DONE IT!

Eight weeks done! Congratulations on completing your journal!

The single most important thing you can do now is to *look back* and make a conscious effort to review your achievements over those 8 weeks.

When you started this journal, you set yourself goals and wanted to feel better about one or more aspects of your life.

Go back to pages 4 and 8 and take a detailed look at your Wheel of Life and the Goals which you set for yourself. Think about how you felt when you completed them and what you wanted to work towards.

Now complete a new Wheel of Life (overleaf), from how you feel *today*. This is an opportunity for you to notice any similarities and differences from when you completed it 8 weeks ago, and it is also a chance to ask yourself some questions.

MY WHEEL OF LIFE: TAKE TWO

COMPLETED ON:_____

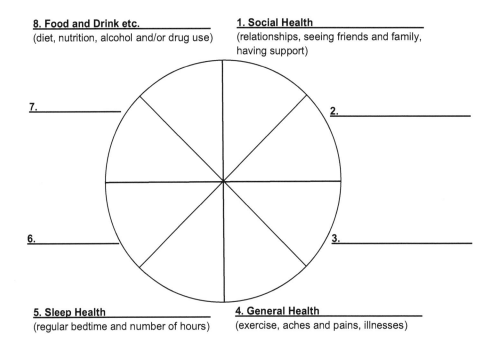

8. Food and Drink etc.
(diet, nutrition, alcohol and/or drug use)

1. Social Health
(relationships, seeing friends and family, having support)

7._____

2._____

6._____

3._____

5. Sleep Health
(regular bedtime and number of hours)

4. General Health
(exercise, aches and pains, illnesses)

What has changed?

What has stayed the same?

What have you achieved?
(have you added it to your Reverse Bucket List?)

Which areas will you keep working on?

What has been the best part of this process?

What have you found difficult?

What are you going to take from this process?

If you haven't quite reached one or more of your goals, now is not the time to give up. Continue to focus on those goals and once completed, set yourself some new ones!

If you haven't already done so, you might now feel ready to share your goals with someone you trust. Having the support and encouragement of others can help you to achieve your goals sooner, but do remember they are *your* goals, and you should continue to work towards them *your* way.

To continue with your journaling, there are many options out there including bullet journals, diaries, guided journals, quote-a-day diaries and also apps for your device. Have a look around and on the app stores to find the right one(s) for you…or buy another one of these!

Whatever you choose to do next, remember to keep checking back to remind yourself how far you have come.

Good luck with the next part of your journey and thank you for choosing to use this journal.

AND FINALLY

Thought colouring in was just for kids? It requires both sides of the brain. While logic helps you keep inside the lines, choosing your colours needs creativity, so it can be a great way to relax your mind and give yourself a well-earned break.

So grab yourself some coloured pencils and have a go on this owl; the symbol of *knowledge, wisdom, good judgement...and change.*

ABOUT THE AUTHOR

Katy Sheridan, together with her husband Dave, established Maximum Edge after identifying significant gaps in provision of life-skills training which improve both mental and physical health.

Their combined professional experience across different sectors has helped them to develop bespoke training programmes which challenge, motivate, educate and encourage individuals to unlock their potential and that of the people around them.

They bring their expertise to numerous companies and organisations to assist in the development of people – from service users to managing directors and everyone in between.

For more information, please visit www.maximumedge.org.uk

If you always do what you've always done,

you'll always get what you always got.

Printed in Great Britain
by Amazon